Old Jacket, New Jacket

by Elliott K. Goldberg

illustrated by Angela Adams

Mom held up a faded
blue jacket.
"This jacket looks like it will
fit you, Iris," said Mom.

Iris looked at the jacket.
It was her sister's old jacket.
Dana always wore it
with her jeans.

Iris shook her head.
"I don't want that old thing,"
said Iris.
"I want a *new* jacket
to wear with my jeans."

"But this is a good jacket,"
said Mom.
"It will look good on you, Iris."

At first, Iris felt sad.
Then she felt mad.
Dana's old jacket was
not the same as a new one.
Iris wanted a jacket
that was just for her.

Iris stared at the jacket.
She wanted to make it special.
What could she do?
She put a heart pin on it.
That didn't look right.
But the pin gave Iris an idea.

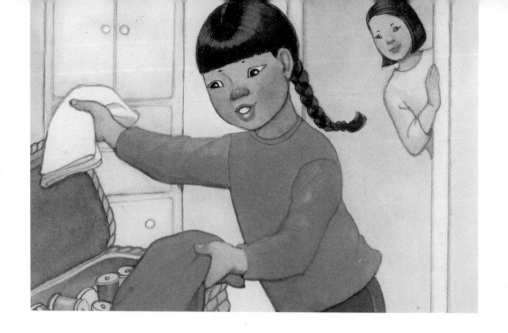

"Mom, can I use some things
in your sewing box?" Iris asked.

"Sure," said Mom.

Iris opened the sewing box.
She took out some red cloth
and some white cloth.

She cut the red cloth in the shape of a heart.

"Oh, I see what you are doing," her mom said.
"Do you want some help?"

9

"Yes, please," said Iris.
"I want red hearts
and white stars."

"Okay," said Mom.
"You cut out the hearts.
I'll sew them on."

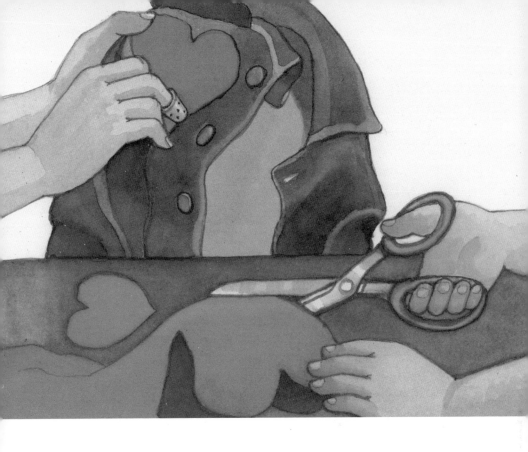

Iris cut out three red hearts.
Her mom put one heart
on the back of the jacket.
She put two hearts
on the front of the jacket.

Then Mom cut out lots of stars.
She put them on the front of
the jacket and on the back, too.

Iris looked at the jacket
and started to feel happy!

Mom took some gold beads
out of a jar.
"Would you like some beads
on your jacket?" she asked.

"Oh, yes!" said Iris.
"Red hearts and white stars
and gold beads.
That will be beautiful!"

"Here is your new jacket,"
Mom said to Iris at last.

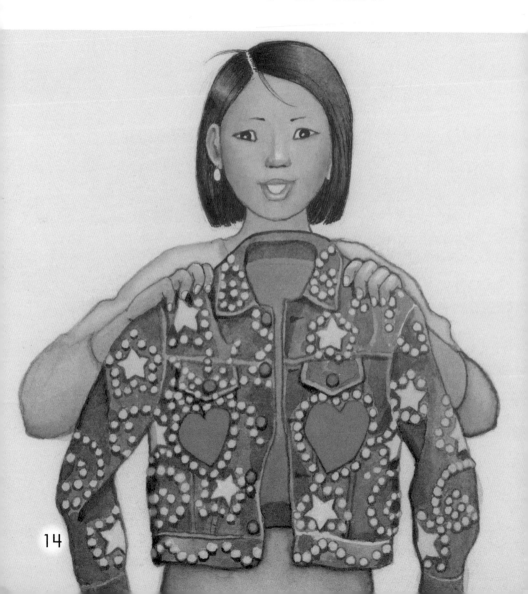

14

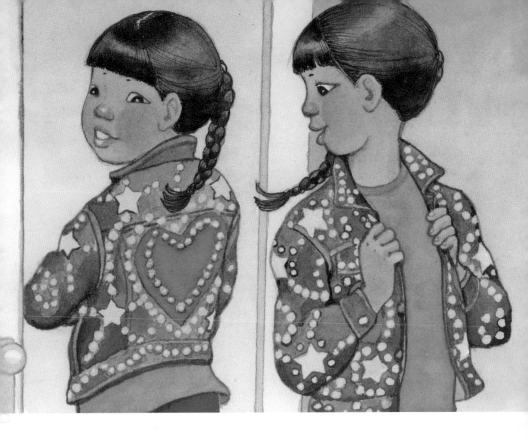

Iris put on the jacket.
She looked at the back,
and she looked at the front.
She liked what she saw.
Iris **loved** her new jacket.

Just then Dana came in.
"Nice jacket!" said Dana.
"Can I have one, too?"
she asked Mom.

"It's easy," said Iris.
"Just get an old jacket
and make it brand new!"